Meginley

modern patterns
ILLUSIONS
coloring book

MindWare®
brainy toys for kids of all ages®

www.MINDWAREonline.com

A MindWare® Original!

Our entire selection of Brainy Toys for Kids of All Ages® is available at www.MINDWAREonline.com, or by calling us at 800-999-0398 to request a catalog.

Coloring Books

Each of our coloring books offer one of a kind patterns, textures and styles you make your own by choosing how to bring them to life.

Animal Habitats Series

Creature Camouflage Series

Designs Series

Lights Series

Modern Patterns Series

Mosaics Series

Quilts Series

Scapes Series

Transformations Series

Puzzle Books

Our puzzle books build skills in many areas—from logic to math, spatial reasoning to verbal skills.

Addition Adventures

Analogy Challenges

Clip Clues

Code Breakers

Deducibles

Directive Detective

Division Designs

Fast Fact Trivia

Grid Perplexors

Logic Links

Math Path Puzzles

Math Perplexors

More Multiplication Mosaics

Multiplication Mosaics

Noodlers

Number Junctions

Perplexors

Sequencers

Subtraction Secrets

Tactic Twisters

Tan-Tastic Tangrams

Venn Perplexors

Word Winks

Word Wise

Games and Activities

Building blocks to strategic games, mystery puzzles to imaginative play — enhance abstract thinking and reasoning skills with our ingenious games and activities.

Bella's Mystery Decks

Blik-Blok

Block Buddies

Chaos

Cross-Eyed

Flip 4

Gambit

Hue Knew?

Logic Links Game

Make Your Own Mask Kit

Noodlers Game

Pattern Play

Qwirkle

Tally Rally

Squzzles

Configure nine 3 x 3 pieces into a square where all images match up on every single side. Three challenging puzzles per box.

3-D Scramblers

Animal Babies

Creature Kingdom

Creepy Crawlers

Illusions

Insect Infested

Nocturnal Animals

Optical Illusions

Play Ball!

Wings & Wheels

World Money

EAN 978-1-933054-53-7
SKU 36017

brainy toys for kids of all ages®

for other MindWare products visit our website
www.MINDWAREonline.com

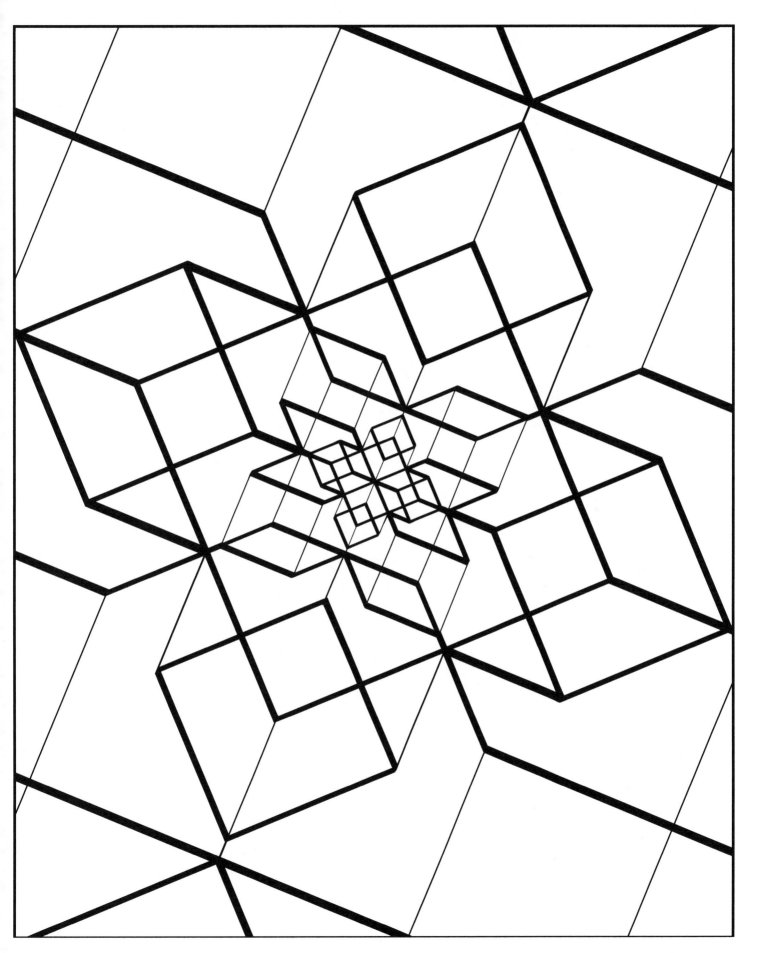

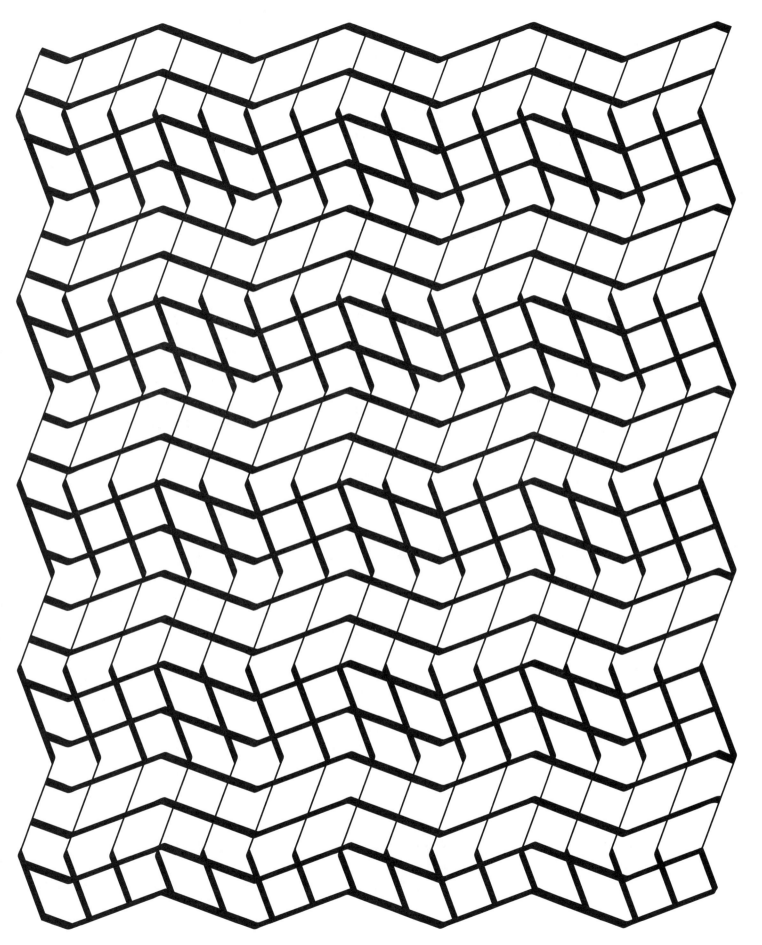

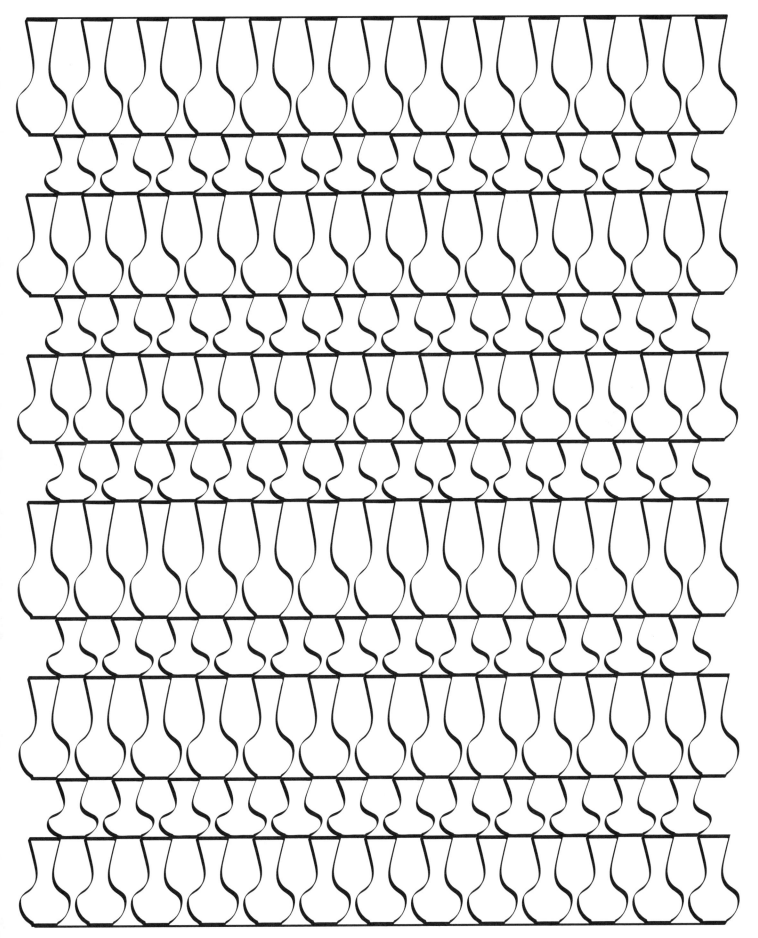

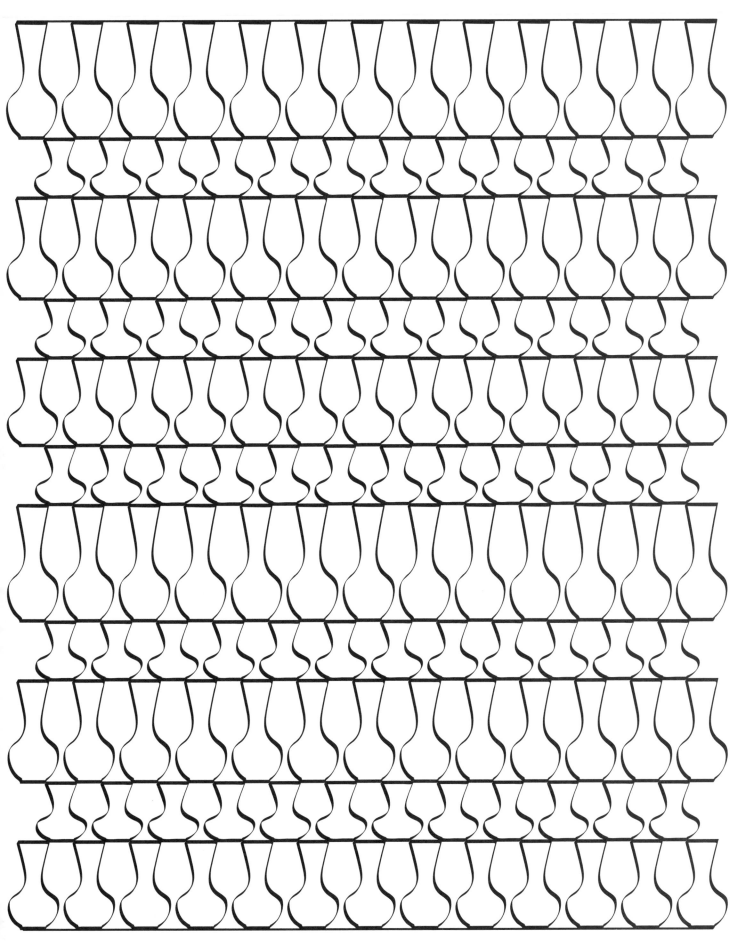